KU-754-003

Contents

Page

MY READY-TO-READ STORIES

ILLUSTRATED BY PAMELA STOREY

STORIES BY JUNE WOODMAN

BRIMAX BOOKS · NEWMARKET · ENGLAND

Here is a collection of amusing animal
stories with a very simple repetitive
text primarily designed for children of
4–7 years who are ready to read.
The text is presented in large type.
In addition to each story is a special
section to encourage the revision of
new words and concepts to stimulate
observation and memory.
Children will love the easy to read
stories of the Dizzy Ducklings,
Dinky Deer, Merry Mole, Ozzie Owl,
Polly Pig and their friends.

ISBN 0 86112 433 2
© BRIMAX BOOKS LTD 1987. All rights reserved.
Published by BRIMAX BOOKS, Newmarket, England 1987
Reprinted 1991
Produced by Mandarin Offset
Printed in Hong Kong

THREE DIZZY DUCKLINGS

Dilly Duck and her three
little ducklings are going
out for the day.
"We are going to the zoo,"
says Dilly.
"I like the elephants,"
says Daffy duckling.
"I like the penguins,"
says Dandy duckling.
"I like the funny monkeys,"
says Dippy duckling.

11

Here comes Hoppy Rabbit in his little car.

"Hop in," he says. They set off for the zoo. On the way, they meet Cuddly Cat, Merry Mole and Flippy Frog. "We want to go too," they say. So they get into the car. Then they meet Paddy Dog, Bossy Bear and Ozzie Owl. They all get into the car.

The car is full.
"Do not fall out," says
Dilly to her ducklings.
It is not far to the zoo.
Soon they arrive.
They all go inside.
"Keep together," says Dilly.
"Do not go too near to
the wild animals," says
Hoppy Rabbit.
They all go to look at the
lions and tigers.

The lions and tigers roar.
The ducklings are afraid.
They all run away.
"That lion is very big," says
Cuddly Cat.
"So is the tiger," says
Paddy Dog.
"Where are my three little
ducklings?" says Dilly.
"I cannot see them."

They all go to look for
the three little ducklings.
They look for them by the
giraffe house. The giraffes
are very tall. No one
can see the ducklings.
"They may have gone to see
the hippos," says Merry Mole.
So they all go to have a look.

19

The little ducklings are
not at the hippo house.
"The hippos are VERY big,"
says Flippy.
"But my ducklings are only
little," says Dilly.
Bossy thinks they may be
with the zebras. So they
go to have a look. But
the ducklings are not
there. Dilly begins to cry.

21

"You are silly," says Hoppy,
"Daffy likes the elephants.
We will look there."
So they go to the elephant
house. They see three big
elephants and one baby.
They see Daffy, too. Daffy
is running after the baby.
The baby is cross. It gets
Daffy with its trunk.
It swings Daffy round and
round. Then it drops Daffy.
BUMP!

23

Daffy begins to cry.
"I am dizzy," says Daffy.
"You are silly," says Dilly.
Flippy Frog says that Dandy
likes the penguins. So they
go to the penguin pool.
They see the penguins.
They see Dandy too. He is in
the pool. Dandy is going
round and round on
a little penguin's back.

"Come to me!" says Dilly.
When Dandy gets out, he falls
down. BUMP!
He is dizzy and he begins
to cry.
"Dippy likes the monkeys,"
says Bossy Bear.
So they all go to look for
the monkey house. Daffy and
Dandy walk round and round.
They are still dizzy.

They find the funny monkeys.
They find Dippy, too. He is
inside with the monkeys.
They are running after him.
Round and round they go.
Then they catch up with him.
They throw him out. BUMP!
"Come to me!" says Dilly.
But he walks round and round.
"I am dizzy," he says.
He is crying too.

"Stop it!" says Dilly. "You were all very silly."
They feel tired so they go and sit down at some little tables. They have some drinks and something to eat.
They all feel better.
Then they walk round to see all the animals again.

But Dippy goes to see the elephants, not the monkeys. Daffy goes to see the penguins, not the big elephants. Dandy goes to see the monkeys, not the penguins. The lions roar, the zebras run and the giraffes look down at them. The hippos yawn.

"Home time," says Dilly.

When they get home, the
three little ducklings
jump into the pond. They
begin to swim. But they go
round and round and round.
They do look funny.
"You are still dizzy," says
Dilly Duck.
What silly
          dizzy
             ducklings!

35

Say these words again

zoo	round
full	drops
together	penguin
near	catch
animals	tired
lost	tables
trunk	elephant

What are they doing?

yawning

roaring

crying

swimming

running

DINKY DEER IS LOST

Dinky Deer is in the forest.
She is looking for her mother.
"I am lost," she says.
"I cannot find my mother."
Dinky Deer is all alone in
the dark forest. She is not
very happy.
"I must find my mother,"
she says. Dinky sets off
to look for her.

Dinky jumps out onto the forest path. Cuddly Cat is on the path.

"OH!" says Cuddly.

She drops her basket, and all her cakes fall out.

"I am lost," says Dinky.

"Have one of my cakes," says Cuddly. "Then we will go and find your mother."

They pick up the rest of the cakes, then they go off together. Soon they come to the duck pond. Dilly Duck is there. She is very cross.

"Look at my three silly little ducklings," she says. The ducklings are by the pond. It is very muddy. The ducklings are muddy too. Dilly washes them clean.

"I am lost," says Dinky to
the three ducklings.
"We will help you," they
all say.
"I will help too," says Dilly.
So Dinky Deer, Cuddly Cat,
Dilly and her ducklings
all set off to look for
Mother Deer.
Soon they come to Bossy
Bear's house. He is washing
his windows.

The three little ducklings
run up to Bossy. They make
him jump and he drops his
bucket. The water falls out
all over Dilly Duck.
"OH!" says Dilly. "You are
silly little ducklings!" She is
all wet and VERY cross.
"I am lost," says Dinky.
"I will help you," says Bossy.

49

So they all set off to
look for Mother Deer.
Dinky and Cuddly Cat,
Dilly and her ducklings
and Bossy Bear all go
down the lane together.
Soon they come to Paddy
Dog's house. He is busy
painting his gate.
The three little ducklings
run up to him.

"Dinky Deer is lost!" they
call out. It makes Paddy jump.
He drops the paint, and it
goes all over them.
"OH!" say the ducklings.
Dilly Duck is VERY cross.
"I cannot find my mother,"
says Dinky. "I am lost."
She is very sad.
"I will help you," says
Paddy Dog.

So Dinky Deer, Cuddly Cat,
Dilly and her ducklings,
Bossy Bear and Paddy Dog
all set off together.
Soon they come to Hoppy
Rabbit's house. He is
very busy washing his
little car.
The ducklings run to him.
They make him jump and he
falls over his bucket. Now
he is wet and cross.
But Dinky Deer is sad.

Dinky tells Hoppy Rabbit
that she is lost.
"I will help you," says Hoppy.
So Dinky Deer, Cuddly Cat,
Dilly and her ducklings,
Bossy Bear, Paddy Dog and
Hoppy Rabbit all go off together
"Look up there!" says Paddy.
They look up into a tree.
They see Ozzie Owl. He is
asleep. The three little
ducklings run to the tree.

"Dinky Deer is lost!" they
call. They make him jump.
Ozzie Owl falls out of the tree.
"OW!" he says. He is very cross
"Have you seen Mother Deer?"
says Cuddly Cat.
"She is in the forest," says
Ozzie. "Come with me."
So Dinky, Cuddly, Dilly,
the ducklings, Bossy, Paddy,
Hoppy and Ozzie go to the
forest together.

Merry Mole and Flippy Frog
are in the forest. They are
busy picking blackberries.
The ducklings run up to them.
"Dinky Deer is lost!" they
call. Merry and Flippy
fall into the bush.
"OW!" they say.
The blackberries all fall
out of their basket.
"You three are silly!"
say Merry and Flippy.

Dinky Deer begins to cry.
"I am lost," she says.
"I cannot find my mother!"
"LOOK!" say Merry and Flippy.
Someone is coming round the
blackberry bush.
It is Mother Deer.
"Here I am, Dinky," she says.
"You are not lost now. Do not
cry, little Dinky."

Now Dinky is very happy.
Mother Deer is happy, too.
Merry and Flippy pick up
all the blackberries and
the ducklings help them.
Then they all sit down
under the trees together.
They eat the cakes
and blackberries.
"Thank you," says Dinky to
all her friends, "I am not
lost now!"

Say these words again

lost	muddy
alone	helps
own	bucket
jumps	blackberries
drops	asleep
basket	happy
together	here

What are they doing?

washing

eating

crying

falling

painting

POLLY PIG and THE BEE

Polly Pig wants some sweets. There are no sweets in the jar. Polly Pig likes sweets.
"I will go to the shop," says Polly Pig. "I will buy some more sweets."
The bee likes sweets. "I will go to the shop with Polly Pig," says the bee.

Polly Pig puts on her hat.
She is ready to go.
Polly Pig shuts the door.
The bee is outside.
"Go away bee," says Polly
Pig.
"Buzz!" says the bee. "I
want some sweets."
"There are no sweets,"
says Polly Pig. "Go away!"

Polly Pig goes down the hill. She sees Bob Hedgehog.

"Where are you going?" says Bob Hedgehog.

"To the shop to buy some sweets," says Polly Pig.

"I will buy some too," says Bob Hedgehog. "Can I go with you?"

"Yes, you can," says Polly Pig.

The bee goes after them.
"Go away bee," says Polly
Pig.
"What does the bee
want?" says Bob
Hedgehog.
"Buzz!" says the bee. "I
want some sweets."
"We have no sweets," says
Bob Hedgehog. "Go
away."
The bee buzzes. The bee is
cross.

Little Hamster is sitting on the fence.
"Where are you going?" says Little Hamster.
"To the shop, to buy some sweets," says Polly Pig.
"I will buy some too," says Little Hamster. "Can I come with you?"
"Yes, you can," says Polly Pig.

Little Hamster gets down from the fence. They all go along the road. The bee goes too.

"Go away bee," says Polly Pig.

"What does the bee want?" says Little Hamster.

"Buzz!" says the bee. "I want some sweets."

"We have no sweets," says Little Hamster. "Go away."

They go into the shop.
They shut the door. The
bee is outside. Cheepy
Chick is in the shop.
"What do you want?" says
Cheepy Chick.
"I want to buy some
sweets," says Polly Pig.
"So do I," says Bob
Hedgehog.
"So do I," says Little
Hamster.

83

The shop is full of jars. The jars are full of sweets. There are yellow ones, brown ones, white ones, pink ones and green ones. "Which sweets do you want?" says Cheepy Chick.

"I will have yellow sweets," says Polly Pig. Cheepy Chick goes up the ladder. She gets the jar. She brings it down. She puts some sweets in a bag. "I will have green sweets," says Bob Hedgehog. "I will have white sweets," says Little Hamster.

Polly Pig pays for her
sweets.
Bob Hedgehog pays for his
sweets.
Little Hamster pays for his
sweets.
The bee is looking at them.
"Will that be all?" says
Cheepy Chick.
"Yes, thank you," they say.
"Goodbye," says Cheepy
Chick. She opens the door.
"Come again," says
Cheepy Chick.

The bee is waiting.
"Go away bee," says Polly
Pig.
"Buzz!" says the bee. "I
want some sweets."
"Go away," says Bob
Hedgehog.
"Buzz!" says the bee. "I
want some sweets".
"Go away," says Little
Hamster.
"Buzz!" says the bee. "I
want some sweets."

"You cannot have any of my sweets," says Polly Pig.

"You cannot have any of my sweets," says Bob Hedgehog.

"You cannot have any of my sweets," says Little Hamster.

"Please," buzzed the bee.

"Please, can I have some sweets?"

"Yes, now you have said 'Please', that is the proper way to ask," says Polly Pig. "I will give you some sweets."
Bob Hedgehog gives the bee some sweets.
Little Hamster gives the bee some sweets.
The bee says, "Thank you! Thank you! Thank you!"

Say these words again

buy
buzzes
sitting
waiting
outside
please
ready

goes
jars
goodbye
thank you
which
pays
again

What can you see?

shop

fence

door

sweets

bee

CHEEPY CHICK'S HOLIDAY

Cheepy Chick has a shop. The shop is full of jars. The jars are full of sweets. There are yellow ones, brown ones, white ones, pink ones and green ones. Cheepy Chick sells a lot of sweets. Cheepy Chick is always busy.

101

Rob Rabbit wants brown sweets. They are on the top shelf.

Cheepy Chick gets the ladder. Up she goes. She gets the jar. She brings it down.

Cheepy Chick puts some brown sweets in a bag.

Rob Rabbit pays for the sweets.

"Thank you," says Rob Rabbit.

Cheepy Chick puts the jar
back on the shelf. She
comes down the ladder.
Molly Mouse comes into
the shop. Molly Mouse
wants to buy pink sweets.
They are on the middle
shelf.
Cheepy Chick moves the
ladder along.

Cheepy Chick goes up the ladder. She gets the jar from the shelf.
"I do not want pink sweets now," says Molly Mouse.
"I want white ones."
The white sweets are on the next shelf. Cheepy Chick comes down the ladder. She moves the ladder along. She goes up the ladder.

Polly Pig comes to the shop. Little Hamster and Bob Hedgehog come with her. Cheepy Chick is asleep.

"Wake up," says Polly Pig.

"Are you ill?" says Little Hamster.

"I have been very busy," says Cheepy Chick. "I am so tired."

"You need a holiday," says Polly Pig.

"Who will look after the shop?" says Cheepy Chick.
"I will look after the shop," says Polly Pig.
"I will help Polly," says Little Hamster.
"So will I," says Bob Hedgehog.
"Go and get ready," says Polly Pig.
Cheepy Chick gets ready to go. Cheepy Chick is happy.

Cheepy Chick packs her bag. She puts in her hat. She puts in her scarf. She puts in her coat. She is ready to go.

Polly Pig stands at the door. She waves goodbye. Little Hamster waves goodbye. Bob Hedgehog waves goodbye.

They all say, "Have a good time."

Cheepy Chick is on a train. It goes a long way. Cheepy Chick sits by the window. She looks out of the window. She can see snow. It looks cold. Cheepy Chick likes the snow. "I will be there soon," says Cheepy Chick. Cheepy Chick is happy.

Cheepy Chick has lots of fun. She likes the snow. The snow is cold. Cheepy Chick is not cold.
Her hat keeps her warm.
Her scarf keeps her warm.
Her coat keeps her warm.
Cheepy Chick falls over.
The snow is soft. She is not hurt. It is fun.

Pat Penguin helps Cheepy Chick. He shows her what to do. Cheepy Chick goes very fast. She can stop when she wants to. She does not fall over.

"I like going fast," says Cheepy Chick.

"I like being on holiday," says Cheepy Chick.

119

Cheepy Chick sends a card
to the shop. Little Hamster
reads it. It says, "Wish you
were here."
"So do I," says Polly Pig.
"So do I," says Little
Hamster.
"So do I," says Bob
Hedgehog.

Cheepy Chick is home again. Polly Pig is glad to see her. Little Hamster is glad to see her. Bob Hedgehog is glad to see her.
"We have been so busy," they say.
"We feel tired now," they say.

Cheepy Chick does not feel
tired. She does not need
the ladder. She hops up to
the jars of sweets.
"My holiday did me good,"
says Cheepy Chick.
"We can see that," says
Polly Pig.
They are all happy.

Say these words again

sweets	snow
full	cold
goodbye	busy
middle	thank you
holiday	tired
waves	happy
window	ready